ANNUAL 2011

Pippa Funnell

ANNUAL 2011

Illustrated by Jennifer Miles

Orion
Children's Books

First published in Great Britain in 2010
by Orion Children's Books
a division of the Orion Publishing Group Ltd
Orion House
5 Upper St Martin's Lane
London WC2H 9EA
An Hachette UK Company

1 3 5 7 9 8 6 4 2

A catalogue record for this book is available from the British Library.

ISBN 978 1 4440 0111 2

Printed and bound in Italy by Rotolito Lombarda

www.orionbooks.co.uk
www.tillysponytails.co.uk

Contents

Hi Everyone!

Welcome to my first ever Annual. It's packed with my favourite photos and top tips, plus brilliant quizzes and activities, as well as extracts from the *Tilly's Pony Tails* books and even a peek at Tilly's top secret diary!

There's something in here for pony lovers everywhere – enjoy!

Love,

Pippa
x

A Day on Silver Shoe Farm

PIPPA SAYS

Silver Shoe Farm is just the sort of place I loved going when I was young – and I still do! There are all sorts of horses there, from ponies to competition horses, and the farm is always bustling with activity.

For anyone who loves horses like Tilly does, there's nothing more exciting than feeling part of a team at somewhere like Silver Shoe Farm. Here's what she gets up to on a typical day at the farm.

Arriving

However early I arrive, there's always lots going on. Some of the horses have their heads out over the stable doors, waiting for some attention or a tasty treat. Others are being tacked up, or led through the yard for a few hours out in the paddock.

Angela usually meets me. She owns the farm with her father, Jack Fisher. Angela's brilliant, and Duncan is too. He's the head-boy at Silver Shoe and helps Angela run the stables. They're both great jockeys. I'd love to be as good as them one day.

Mucking Out

First of all, I muck out. It's not the most glamorous job in the world, but if you love horses, you really don't mind! It's important for the horses to have food, clean water and fresh bedding, and we want them to be happy and comfortable.

Grooming

Mia and I spend a lot of time grooming our pony, Rosie. We brush her coat, comb her mane and tail, and pick out her hooves and put hoof oil on them. She really enjoys it, and she looks beautiful when we've finished.

Tacking Up and Riding

Before I have a lesson or go for a hack, I always groom first, then tack up. Sometimes I have a riding lesson in the sand school or I practise jumping in the outside arena.

When we finish riding, I remove the tack, and make sure it's all clean before neatly hanging it in the tack room. And of course I ensure Rosie is brushed off, even washed off if she's sweaty – we learned very early that you should never leave dry sweat on your pony.

Feeding

We always make sure the ponies have a constant supply of clean, fresh water. You wouldn't believe how much horses drink! We fill the hay-nets for the ponies, but how much hay and what kind of food they get varies according to their weight and what kind of work they're doing. Angela always oversees feeding and advises us.

Chilling Out

After working hard, we relax in the club room. In the summer we drink homemade lemonade, and in winter we warm up with big mugs of hot chocolate. If we're lucky, Angela makes her special flapjacks!

Tilly loves her days with the horses at Silver Shoe Farm!

Tilly's Pony Tales Wordsearch

All these ponies and horses appear in *Tilly's Pony Tails*, and some will appear in Tilly's new adventures, coming soon!

ALADDIN ✓
LULABELLE ✓
NEPTUNE ✓
NIMROD ✓
ROSIE ✓

SAMSON ✓
SOLO ✓
THUMBELINA ✓
BUNNY ✓
MOONSHADOW ✓

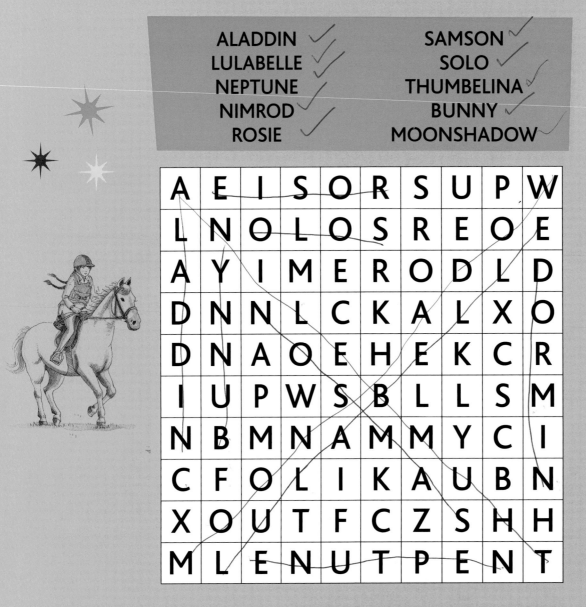

A	E	I	S	O	R	S	U	P	W
L	N	O	L	O	S	R	E	O	E
A	Y	I	M	E	R	O	D	L	D
D	N	N	L	C	K	A	L	X	O
D	N	A	O	E	H	E	K	C	R
I	U	P	W	S	B	L	L	S	M
N	B	M	N	A	M	M	Y	C	I
C	F	O	L	I	K	A	U	B	N
X	O	U	T	F	C	Z	S	H	H
M	L	E	N	U	T	P	E	N	T

When you've completed the puzzle, look for the hidden name. Start at the top left and write down all the leftover letters, moving from left to right, then down to the next row. Fill them in below to reveal the name of the horse who won team Silver with Pippa at the 2000 Olympics.

— — — — — — — —   — — — — —

14

My Top Secret Diary
By Tiger Lily Redbrow

Saturday 5th March 2011

I can't believe how much my life has changed. Not long ago, I just looked at horses in books and magazines. Now I can go to Silver Shoe Farm whenever I want and see all the beautiful horses, especially Magic Spirit and Rosie. It's like a dream come true!

I've made two new friends too – Cally and Mia – who love horses just as much as I do. Becky's still my best friend, of course, even though she says I'm more horse-mad than ever. She's right!

I had a brilliant day at the farm today. Angela gave me a riding lesson on Rosie. And she said I'd done really well!!! I gave Rosie lots of attention after that.

Maybe my special bracelet is bringing me good luck and helping me with my riding lessons? One of the girls at the farm asked me about it today. When I told her I'd had it since I was born and that I was adopted, she looked surprised and a little bit sorry for me. But I don't care. The Redbrows are my number one family and Mum and Dad are the best parents in the world. I've just got another family too, that's all. I think it must be a lucky bracelet, and all my favourite horses seem to like it too!

Tilly's Bracelet

Tilly's bracelet was strange looking, made from woven horsehairs – black, plaited like Tilly's hair, and linked with a small silver clasp. Tilly had worn the bracelet all her life.

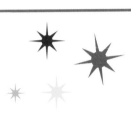

PIPPA SAYS

The idea for Tilly's bracelet came when I was playing with a horsehair bracelet from a horse that I'd evented called Viceroy. Tragically he died of colic, so the owners sent some of his hair off to be woven into bracelets in his memory. Looking at this reminded me of friendship bracelets I'd made when I was younger, and it was such a lovely link to a special horse that I thought it would be perfect for Tilly!

Make Your Very Own Horsehair Bracelet

Don't do anything dangerous – why not collect hair from the brushes after grooming, or use embroidery thread? We don't want lots of ponies going around without any tails! You could make one for your friend too.

You will need

Embroidery thread or horsehairs
Scissors
Sticky tape

1 Cut nine strands of embroidery thread or horsehair, each about 50 cm long.

2 Tie all the threads together with a knot at the top.

3 Tape the knotted end to something firm and flat, like a table or a chopping board.

4 Divide the threads into three sections, and start plaiting – just like you'd plait your hair.

5 When the bracelet is long enough to go around your wrist with some length to spare, tie a knot in the end.

6 Wrap the bracelet around your wrist and tie the two knotted ends together – your bracelet is complete!

TILLY'S TOP TIP

Always wear your bracelet when you're riding

60 Seconds with Pippa

Name: Pippa Funnell

Date of Birth: 7th October 1968

Place of Birth: Crowborough, East Sussex

Job: Equestrian sportswoman and writer

Star sign: Libra

Hi Pippa, can you tell us which are your favourites from the following...

Riding or writing?

Riding

Dressage or showjumping?

Showjumping

Cricket or rugby?

Rugby

Caspian or Connemara?

Connemara

Getting up early or late?

Early!

Black Beauty or National Velvet?

Black Beauty

Cats or dogs?

Dogs – especially Jack Russells

Badminton or Burghley?

Badminton

Grey or Bay?

Bay – greys are more difficult to keep clean!

Shetland or Shire?

Shetland – because it doesn't hurt so much when they tread on your toes!

What quick-fire questions would you like to ask Pippa? Send them in to the website.

www.tillyponystails.co.uk

18

Pippa's Top Tips for Spring

PIPPA SAYS

I love the spring – with all the daffodils and other flowers, new leaves on the trees and longer daylight hours. And also the anticipation for competitions and the riding season ahead! Take some time and follow my tips to ensure you and your pony are in the very best condition.

Riding

- Build your pony's fitness up gradually. Your riding may have been restricted during winter because of the cold weather and nights drawing in, so be careful not to overdo it.
- Start with hacking and slower work before you charge around and try jumping lots of fences.
- Don't forget to check your pony's legs for cuts or swellings, and get these sorted out before you start riding.

Grooming

- One of the worst things about spring is when your pony's winter coat starts falling out – the hair sticks to everything, especially the numnah!
- Get rid of the excess hair by grooming your pony with a rubber curry comb – and don't forget the numnah will need regular washing and brushing too!
- It's essential to worm your pony three to four times a year. You should also get his teeth checked twice a year. Ask at your stables for advice.

Stabling

- As the weather improves, ponies enjoy spending more time out in the field.
- Most ponies like company. If there aren't any other ponies, they're sometimes happy to share with a few sheep, cows or even a goat.
- Always make sure the paddock field has a fresh supply of water and good, safe fencing.

Feeding

- There's plenty of grass in spring, but don't let your pony eat too much or he could become too fat or even get laminitis, which can cause lameness.
- It's just as dangerous for your pony to be overweight as it is for him to be undernourished.
- If you're concerned, you could fence off an area in the field where the grass has already been eaten and move your pony there for a while.
- If your pony is working hard, he might need a bit more hard feed than usual. Ask for advice if you're unsure.

Horses need special care all year round, so check out my tips for Summer on page 31, Autumn on page 43 and Winter on page 57.

Since I was very young I've always loved dogs and horses. Here I've been put in a pot, but not for boiling!

Just about to go riding, aged four

At a show on Flighty, my second pony

Early days riding Lina, a pony that be longed to a friend of my mother's

Hello, Magic

Angela takes a chance when she lets Tilly visit traumatised horse, Magic Spirit. But she already knows that Tilly has a special way with horses…

"Hello, Magic," Tilly murmured. "It's me again. It's Tilly. Don't be frightened."

Magic snorted and shuffled through the wood-chip bed that had been laid down for him, then he stepped forward inquisitively.

"Can I go in?" asked Tilly, looking at Angela.

"In a minute. See how he is first. Remember what my dad said – no one's been able to get near him yet so we mustn't take any risks. It looks like he's eaten some of his hay at least."

Tilly leaned over the door of the barn and reached out her hand, so that Magic, when he was ready, could come and greet her. A minute passed, and then slowly he came closer.

"Hello there," said Tilly in a soft voice, as she stroked his nose. Magic started sniffing at her bracelet, as he'd done the first time they'd met each other.

"That's amazing," whispered Angela, watching from behind. "Amazing."

After a while, Tilly unbolted the bottom half of the stable door.

"I don't think you should do that," cautioned Angela. But in her typical determined way, Tilly had already made up her mind. She pulled open the wooden door just wide enough for her to slip inside. Then she waited. She didn't go in immediately, because she knew that Magic would let her know exactly when he was ready for her to enter his space. He stepped backwards and rubbed his head against the stable wall. Tilly could see the splinters in the wood panels where he'd tried to kick through.

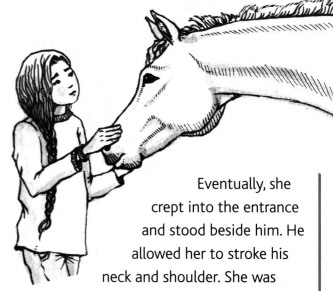

Eventually, she crept into the entrance and stood beside him. He allowed her to stroke his neck and shoulder. She was careful not to touch any sore patches, or make any sudden movements that would frighten him. This was something she knew about from reading lots of pony care books, but she had a different kind of knowledge as well. There was a special connection between them – something that couldn't be learned from any book.

Find out if Magic Spirit recovers his confidence in Magic Spirit the dream horse

Focus on Magic Spirit

Colour: Grey

Breed: Unknown, possibly of Irish origin

Appearance: Tall and athletic, good conformation and big, bold eyes

Personality: Peaceful, happy and relaxed, but also strong, determined and headstrong, a good competitor and a future winner

Special Info: Magic Spirit's best friend is a miniature Shetland pony called Lina – and Tilly, of course!

Magic Spirit wasn't always such a fine horse. If you read *Magic Spirit* you'll discover how he comes to live at Silver Shoe Farm, and how Tilly helps turn him into a dream horse.

Make a Lucky Horseshoe

1 Trace around the horseshoe template on this page, transfer your drawing to the cardboard and cut it out.

2 Either wrap the strips of foil around the horseshoe, or spray it with silver paint. If you use foil strips, glue or tape the ends down.

3 Now make your horseshoe look gorgeous! You could cut out your name in coloured paper and glue it onto the horseshoe, tie ribbons around it or sprinkle on glitter or sequins.

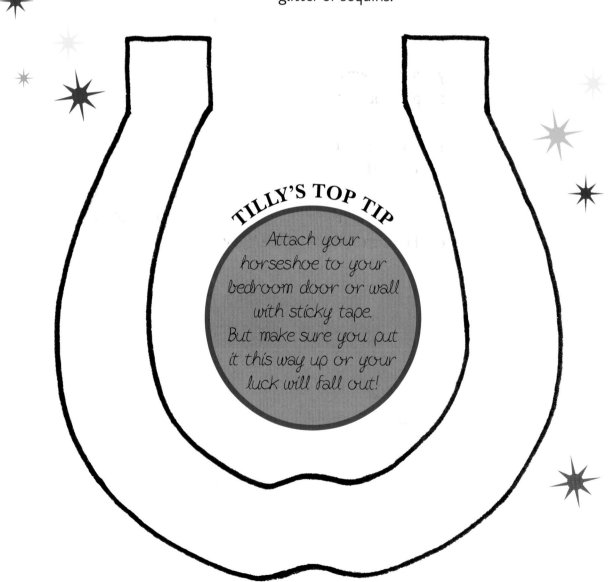

TILLY'S TOP TIP

Attach your horseshoe to your bedroom door or wall with sticky tape. But make sure you put it this way up or your luck will fall out!

Why are horseshoes lucky?

There are all sorts of old superstitions connected to horseshoes. People used to believe that a witch would melt if she walked under a horseshoe, that hiccups could be cured by staring at a horseshoe and wishing the hiccups away, and that horseshoes would keep away nightmares.

But why? There are a number of reasons...

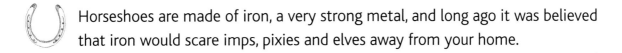 Horseshoes are made of iron, a very strong metal, and long ago it was believed that iron would scare imps, pixies and elves away from your home.

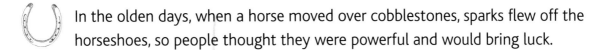 In the olden days, when a horse moved over cobblestones, sparks flew off the horseshoes, so people thought they were powerful and would bring luck.

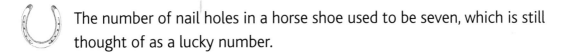 The number of nail holes in a horse shoe used to be seven, which is still thought of as a lucky number.

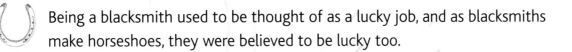 Being a blacksmith used to be thought of as a lucky job, and as blacksmiths make horseshoes, they were believed to be lucky too.

Angela's Top Ten Tacking-Up Tips

PIPPA SAYS

When you first start tacking up and untacking, it can seem very complicated. But don't worry, it'll become easier the more practice you get. Always watch your instructor carefully and follow their lead. Here are Angela's top ten tacking-up tips.

1 Make sure your pony is safely tied before you start tacking up. Use a quick-release knot, so that he doesn't feel constrained.

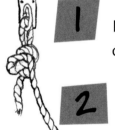

2 When you're putting on the bridle, be careful not to bang your pony's teeth with the bit, as this may worry him.

3 When you buckle up the throat lash, there should be space to fit four fingers between it and your pony's cheek.

4 The bit needs to be the right size and in the right position. Make sure the bit is sitting straight in your pony's mouth. If the bit is correctly fitted you should see a couple of small wrinkles in the corners of his mouth.

5 Ponies' mouths are very sensitive, so ensure the noseband sits just below the cheekbone to avoid any discomfort.

6 When you do up the girth, do it gently and slowly. Then, when you first get on, always check in case the girth has become loose, and tighten it again, if necessary. You don't want the saddle slipping round or back, because this can be dangerous.

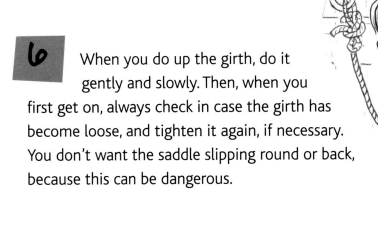

7 Make sure your saddle fits correctly. The most important thing is that it must not come down on the withers and sit too low. Ask for advice.

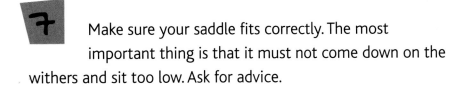

8 Always run up your stirrups before taking your saddle off. If you have a martingale or breastplate, make sure all the straps are undone before you undo the girth.

9 When you take off the bridle, make sure the throat lash and noseband straps are undone first, and gently lower the bit out of your pony's mouth. Allow your pony to drop his head in order to do this.

10 Don't forget – tack must be cleaned regularly with water and saddle soap to keep the leather supple. This keeps the tack safe and in good condition. You should also regularly check the stitching.

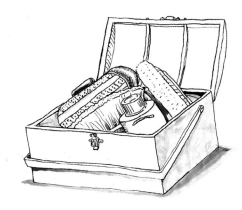

Tack Terms Wordsearch

Can you find all these parts of the saddle and bridle in the wordsearch below?

BROWBAND
CANTLE
CHEEKPIECE
GIRTH
HEADPIECE
KEEPER
NOSEBAND
NUMNAH

PANEL
POMMEL
REIN
SEAT
SKIRT
SNAFFLE
STIRRUPS
THROATLASH

X	T	P	S	R	G	N	C	B	L	E
B	Z	A	P	E	M	U	H	R	E	L
E	U	N	U	I	K	M	E	O	M	F
S	C	T	R	N	H	N	E	W	M	F
K	E	E	R	E	E	A	K	B	O	A
I	L	A	I	L	P	H	P	A	P	N
R	E	M	T	P	T	E	I	N	Q	S
T	N	N	S	R	D	X	E	D	E	Y
F	A	C	I	Z	Q	A	C	K	Z	H
C	P	G	D	N	A	B	E	S	O	N
H	S	A	L	T	A	O	R	H	T	D

28

Find Your Dream Horse

Tilly loves her pony, Rosie, but her dream horse is Magic Spirit. Which of the magnificent horses from *Tilly's Pony Tails* would you love to ride? Follow the flow chart and find out.

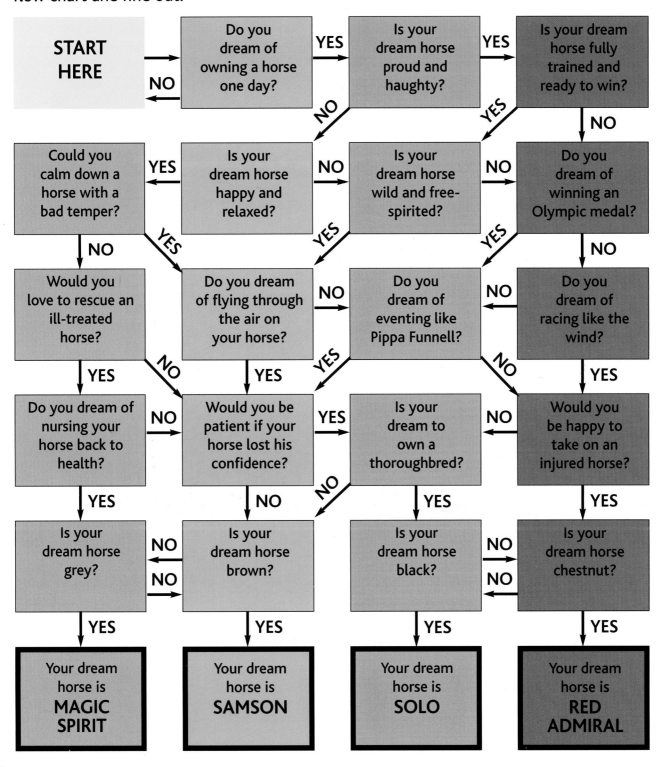

START HERE

Do you dream of owning a horse one day? — YES → Is your dream horse proud and haughty? — YES → Is your dream horse fully trained and ready to win?

NO (loops back)

Is your dream horse proud and haughty? — NO ↓

Is your dream horse fully trained and ready to win? — YES, NO ↓ Do you dream of winning an Olympic medal?

Could you calm down a horse with a bad temper? — YES → Is your dream horse happy and relaxed? — NO → Is your dream horse wild and free-spirited? — NO → Do you dream of winning an Olympic medal?

Could you calm down a horse with a bad temper? — NO ↓

Is your dream horse happy and relaxed? — YES ↓

Is your dream horse wild and free-spirited? — YES ↓

Do you dream of winning an Olympic medal? — NO ↓ Do you dream of racing like the wind?

Would you love to rescue an ill-treated horse?

Do you dream of flying through the air on your horse? — NO → Do you dream of eventing like Pippa Funnell? — NO → Do you dream of racing like the wind?

Would you love to rescue an ill-treated horse? — YES ↓

Do you dream of flying through the air on your horse? — YES ↓

Do you dream of eventing like Pippa Funnell? — YES ↓

Do you dream of racing like the wind? — YES ↓

Do you dream of nursing your horse back to health? — NO → Would you be patient if your horse lost his confidence? — YES → Is your dream to own a thoroughbred? — NO → Would you be happy to take on an injured horse?

Do you dream of nursing your horse back to health? — YES ↓

Would you be patient if your horse lost his confidence? — NO ↓

Is your dream to own a thoroughbred? — NO ↓ YES ↓

Would you be happy to take on an injured horse? — YES ↓

Is your dream horse grey? — NO → Is your dream horse brown? — NO (and NO) → Is your dream horse black? — NO → Is your dream horse chestnut? — NO ←

Is your dream horse grey? — YES ↓

Your dream horse is **MAGIC SPIRIT**

Is your dream horse brown? — YES ↓

Your dream horse is **SAMSON**

Is your dream horse black? — YES ↓

Your dream horse is **SOLO**

Is your dream horse chestnut? — YES ↓

Your dream horse is **RED ADMIRAL**

Breeds Criss-Cross

Can you fit these horse and pony breeds into the criss-cross puzzle below?

4 letters
ARAB
FELL

5 letters
DUTCH
WELSH

6 letters
EXMOOR

7 letters
MUSTANG

8 letters
DARTMOOR
SHETLAND

9 letters
APPALOOSA
CONNEMARA

10 letters
CLYDESDALE

TILLY'S TOP TIP

Fill in the longest word first

Pippa's Top Tips for Summer

PIPPA SAYS

Summer is the perfect time of year for pony lovers. Follow my tips so that you and your pony can be sunny-natured all summer long.

Riding

- There's nothing better than a long ride on a lovely day. But if it's really hot and the ground is baked hard, don't gallop or go too fast. The hard ground can jar your pony's legs, and make them sore.
- Your pony will probably sweat more in the summer, so make sure he is well cooled down after work by washing him.
- Make sure you give your pony a break – he will find work harder in the heat.

Grooming

- Believe it or not, pale ponies can get sunburnt, so apply an equine sun cream, particularly around the nose and mouth.
- Use fly repellent and a mask to keep away all the pesky flies that can really annoy your pony.
- If your pony is hot, cool him down by hosing or sponging him with water.

Stabling

- When it's very hot, it's best to put your pony out in the field at night, and keep him in the stable during the day to avoid the flies and the heat.
- If you don't have stables, make sure there's a shady shelter in your field for your pony.

Feeding

- If it's very dry, there might not be enough grass for your pony, so you'll have to change to hay earlier than usual.
- Don't forget that your pony will be very thirsty, so make sure a supply of cool, clean drinking water is always available.
- Your pony might need some hard food, such as horse and pony nuts, if he's working harder during the summer holidays.

Horses need special care all year round, so check out my tips for Spring on page 19, Autumn on page 43 and Winter on page 57.

Completing my cross-country at Badminton, clear inside the time to maintain the lead on Supreme Rock in 2003, which we went on to win

On Bits and Pieces (Henry) in front of Badminton House

Bits and Pieces
splashing through the
water at Burghley

Rocky and me, with
Emma Lewthwaite his
owner, and Mni My
headgirl, winning the
European Championship

The Cosford Champion Hurdle

Duncan is riding Red Admiral in the Cosford Champion Hurdle, and Tilly, Mia and Cally are there to cheer him on.

"Hello, girls," said a voice behind them. It was Angela. She was wearing a suit and had her hair pinned back with a flower clip. She looked very pretty.

"Hi, Angela."

"Where's Red Admiral?" said Cally, excitedly. "Can we see him?"

"Not right now, I'm afraid. He's in the saddling enclosure. He'll be walked around the parade paddock in twenty minutes. They lead the horses around the paddock before a race so that everyone can view the runners and choose which ones they might place their money on."

"Is Duncan nervous?" asked Mia.

"No, well, at least, if he is, he doesn't show it."

"Do you think he and Red Admiral will win?" asked Tilly.

"Hmm, that's a tricky one. Red Admiral loves firm ground, so the dry weather will suit him. But he hasn't raced for a long time, so that will probably slow him down. We didn't think he'd make it for this race, but weirdly his leg has come right in the nick of time."

Tilly didn't say anything. She just twisted the horsehair bracelet she'd made from Red Admiral's tail and tried to send positive thoughts to him and Duncan.

"Come and join the Silver Shoe crowd in the enclosure, girls. We've got a great view of the finish."

Tilly insisted she wanted to wish Red Admiral luck before the race, so she went to see him being led round the paddock by Jack. His coat was gleaming and he looked majestic. To top it all, he wore the number seven on his saddle cloth – Tilly's lucky number.

Suddenly a bell rang to signal to the jockeys that it was time to mount their horses. There were nerves all round. Jack hoped that Red was fit, plus this was the first race that Duncan was to ride for Silver Shoe Farm – something he had only ever dreamed about.

Do Duncan and Red Admiral win the race? Find out in Red Admiral the racehorse

Focus on Red Admiral

Colour: Chestnut red and white blaze

Breed: Thoroughbred

Appearance: Magnificent looking thoroughbred with beautiful conformation, a very red chestnut with a copper gleam to his coat and a white blaze on his nose

Personality: Proud and haughty, with a regal manner

Special Info: Red Admiral is one of the best horses that Silver Shoe Farm has ever had. His father was a champion and he was born to race

Read **Red Admiral** to find out if this promising horse ever wins a race, and the part Tilly plays in helping him.

Make Your Own Rosette

You will need

Card

Glue

Crepe Paper

Scissors

Felt-tip pens

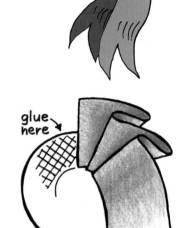

glue here →

1 Cut out two circles of card – one larger circle for the base of the rosette, and a smaller circle for the front of the rosette.

2 Put some glue around the edge of the larger circle.

3 Cut a long strip of crepe paper for the edging of the rosette, then pleat it around the edge of the large circle, catching it in the glue.

4 Keep pleating the crepe paper around the outside edge of the circle until there is no card showing.

5 On the smaller circle, you can write 'FIRST CLASS' or glue on a pony picture.

6 Cut two pieces of crepe paper and make a 'V' in each end, to look like the ribbons in the picture above.

7 Put some glue onto the back of the small circle in the middle and attach the tails, then glue the smaller circle to the middle of the rosette.

8 Press to fix in place and leave to dry.

What colour?

What colour crepe paper have you chosen? The colour of the rosette shows which prize you've won. This differs around the world and from club to club, but a popular order in the UK is:

1st prize – red

2nd prize – blue

3rd prize – yellow

4th prize – green

5th prize – pink

6th prize – brown

My Top Secret Diary
By Tiger Lily Redbrow

Sunday 21st August 2011

Mum and I snuggled up on the sofa last night to watch 'The Horse Whisperer'. I've seen it hundreds of times but I never get bored. It's the most brilliant film and my top favourite. It means even more to me now that I've made a really amazing discovery – I might be a sort of horse whisperer too. Everyone at Silver Shoe Farm says that I have a special gift with horses. I feel so excited and a bit weird too!

People keep asking me what my secret is, but to be honest, I don't know. When I meet a horse, I sort of understand how it's feeling, and I know that we're going to be friends, like with Magic. And if a horse is hurt or in trouble, I feel as though I can help. I don't get scared because I know the horse won't harm me, even if it's badly injured or distressed. I can't even really describe what I do – I just talk quietly and kindly and stroke it gently, and the horse calms down. I forget about everything and everyone else around me. I feel as though I'm in a dream and there's only me and the horse together in the world. If I really were a horse whisperer, wouldn't it be wonderful?

Pippa's Calendar 2011

JANUARY

FEBRUARY

Sunshine Tour, Spain

MAY

Badminton International

Royal Windsor Show

Saumer, France

Chatsworth

Houghton Hall

JUNE

South of England Show

Longleat, Wilts

Bramham

Hickstead, Sussex

SEPTEMBER

Burghley Horse Trials

Blenheim Horse Trials

OCTOBER

Horse of the Year Show

Pau, France

Le Lion, France

Boekelo, Netherlands

Here are some of Pippa's events coming up in 2011.
Why not add in your own events too?

MARCH

Sunshine Tour, Spain (continued)

Great Witchingham

Somerley Park

Tweseldown

APRIL

Burnham Market

Rolex Kentucky

South of England Show

British Open Show Jumping
Championships

JULY

Barbury International Horse Trials

Hickstead, Sussex

Eridge

Brightling Park

AUGUST

Highclere

Gatcombe Park

Young Horse Show Jumping
Champiuonships

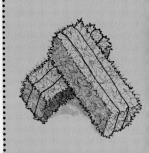

NOVEMBER

Indoor jumping with young horses

DECEMBER

Continued indoor jumping

Olympia Horse Show (watching
rather than riding)

Are You Lost on Planet Pony?

Tilly is absolutely crazy about ponies and horses. Her best friend Becky says that she's on Planet Pony! Are you lost on Planet Pony too? Try this fun quiz and find out.

1. Can you tell from your bedroom that you like ponies?

(a) I've got a pony clock on my bedside table and one pony poster – so far.

(b) I've got pony posters all over my walls.

(c) Every inch of my wall is covered in pony posters, my duvet cover is decorated with horseshoes and my bookcase is full of books about horses and ponies.

2. What's your favourite outfit?

(a) I like girly clothes best – dresses or skirts and lots of glitter.

(b) Jeans, t-shirt and trainers.

(c) Jodhpurs and riding boots, of course!

3. What's your favourite film?

(a) High School Musical

(b) Lord of the Rings

(c) The Horse Whisperer

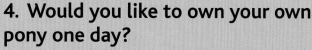

4. Would you like to own your own pony one day?

(a) I like having riding lessons, but I don't want to spend lots of time grooming and mucking out.

(b) Yes, I'd love to have a pony when I'm older.

(c) I don't want just one pony – I want a whole stable full of ponies! It's all I ever dream about.

5. What job would you like to have when you grow up?

(a) I'd like to be a singer or a model.

(b) Maybe an equestrian sportswoman – I'd love to win lots of prizes.

(c) I want to own my own stables, compete professionally and care for injured and neglected horses.

6. How often do you go riding?

(a) I have a lesson at the weekend, but I do lots of other things too so there isn't time for any more riding.

(b) I try to go to the stables to ride a couple of times a week.

(c) As often as possible – I spend every spare minute at the stables.

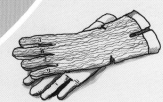

Count up how many (a)s, (b)s and (c)s you scored.
Turn the page to find out how pony-mad you really are!

Mostly (a)s

Your feet are still firmly on Planet Earth! You obviously like ponies and you enjoy your weekly riding lessons, but you've got lots of other hobbies and interests too. So you might peer at Planet Pony through a telescope every now and then, but it's still quite an alien world to you.

Mostly (b)s

You're halfway to Planet Pony, but you've still got one foot on Planet Earth. You like ponies, but you're not completely crazy about them yet. Keep riding whenever you get the chance, and you'll soon find out whether you want to explore Planet Pony further or whether Planet Earth is really the place for you.

Mostly (c)s

Like Tilly, you've travelled to Planet Pony – and there's no coming back! You don't just love horses – you live, breathe and dream about them too! Maybe one day you'll achieve your dream and be a champion rider, like Pippa, or run a busy stables, like Angela. For now, enjoy your horses – but don't forget to visit Planet Earth every now and again!

Pippa's Top Tips for Autumn

PIPPA SAYS

I love riding on bright, crisp autumn days, but sometimes the weather can be unpredictable – so enjoy your riding but take care too.

Riding

- Remember, with the days starting to get shorter and the light fading, make sure you can be seen clearly by other road users when you're out on the roads.
- Always be courteous and thank drivers who slow down with a polite nod or a wave.

Grooming

- When it's wet and muddy, your pony will need extra care and grooming. Don't let your pony's coat get dirty and matted. Spend lots of time brushing your pony to keep his coat in good condition.
- At this time of year, the weather is variable – if your pony gets hot and sweaty, wash him down and give him a good rub with a towel.

Stabling

- Your pony won't mind bad weather as long as you provide somewhere to shelter from the wind and rain. This can be the side of a building, a field shelter, a high hedge or trees.
- Ponies have natural oils in their coat to help keep out the rain. If your pony is staying outside in the autumn, groom lightly so that you don't brush out too much of these protective oils.

Feeding

- There can be a renewed growth in grass during autumn (although it's generally not as rich as spring grass), so be careful to get your pony's feeding balance right.
- You should always feed according to your pony's weight and the amount of exercise he's getting.
- Your pony's weight should stay relatively constant throughout the year, but if he tends to lose weight during the winter months, try to get some extra condition on him in the autumn.

Horses need special care all year round, so check out my tips for Spring on page 19, Summer on page 31 and Winter on page 57.

On Jeremy Fisher at
a Hunter Trial

At a Pony Club
event on Barnaby

A massive drop
with Ensign (Titchie)
in Ireland

Trotting up
at Burghley
with Rainbow
Magic

One Last Ride

Cally has to leave Silver Shoe Farm when she goes to board at Cavendish Hall, and her friends want to make the most of her last day at the farm...

The girls tugged on their fleeces and riding hats and then collected their gear from the tack room. Although they tried hard to be cheerful, a certain sadness hung in the air. It didn't help that Mia kept up a running commentary, saying things like:

"One last tacking up session, one last trot on our favourite forest track..."

Eventually, Cally interrupted her.

"It's not like I'm vanishing, you know! I'm only moving to a school down the road!"

The three girls rode out of the yard and headed down the lane, past the hedgerows, over the bridge, and onto the bridlepath. The leaves had turned. It was a spectacular display or red, orange and yellow. As they walked deeper into the forest, the smell of damp moss filled the air. Squirrels hopped between branches, and in the distance, the sound of a woodpecker echoed through the trees.

"I bet there aren't any rides as nice as this at Cavendish Hall," called Mia.

"I bet there are!" responded Cally.

"Aren't!" protested Mia.

"Are!"

"There are lovely tracks everywhere," said Tilly, wondering why the two best friends were so keen to bicker on their last Silver Shoe Farm hack together.

"Anyway, if Cally finds some cool tracks at

her new school, she'll take us to them, won't she?"

"Deffo," said Cally.

They trotted on in silence, until they came to a large field.

"Couldn't you just?" said Cally, nodding at the stretch of open land.

"You mean..." grinned Mia.

"Let's do it!" they yelled, and then took off together at a canter, laughing and cheering.

Find out what happens when Cally leaves Silver Shoe Farm in Rosie the perfect pony

Focus on Rosie

Colour: Strawberry roan

Breed: Welsh section A cross Connemara

Appearance: Very pretty little pony, a bit tubby, with a scruffy tail

Personality: Lovable, polite, obedient and obliging, with a gentle temperament

Special info: 'Princess Rosie' likes to be pampered – her layer of bedding has to be comfy and thick, fluffed up like pillows for when she lies down

Tilly's friends, Mia and Cally, share Rosie at Silver Shoe Farm. But what happens when Cally leaves for Cavendish Hall? Read *Rosie* to find out.

Ask Pippa

The perfect person to answer all
your horse and pony questions!

Dear Pippa

My pony, Misty, makes a funny noise when I'm near her. My stable manager says it's called 'wickering'. What does it mean when she wickers at me?

Zoe

Dear Zoe

Horse language is fascinating, isn't it? Wickering is a sign of recognition, and mares make this gentle sound to their foals. Misty is telling you that she knows who you are. So, well done, you've made Misty feel safe and secure, and you've obviously put in a lot of time getting to know her and helping her to get to know you. Keep up the good work!

Pippa

Dear Pippa

I've just got a beautiful new horse called Archie, but I'm not sure when he'll need new shoes? How can I tell?

Becky

Dear Becky

That's a very good question, but it's easy to answer. A set of horse shoes normally lasts around five to six weeks. Most good stables will keep a notebook listing all the dates of when the horses were last shod. Ask at the stables when Archie was last shod, and you can work it out from there. Otherwise, look at his feet, and if the shoes look worn and the feet long, it's probably time to shoe him.

Pippa

Dear Pippa

I've read about horses or ponies getting colic and heard it's very serious. I'm worried I won't know whether my horse has it before it's too late. What are the symptoms and what should I do if I spot them?

Georgie

Dear Georgie

If you notice your pony is continuously pawing the ground with a front leg, kicking at his stomach with a hind leg, or turning to look at his tummy, you may well have spotted symptoms of colic. His breathing might become quicker and often he will try to roll. You're right in thinking that colic is very serious, so if you're at all concerned by any of these symptoms, call a vet immediately.

Pippa

Dear Pippa

When my pony bucks, I always seem to fall off, no matter how hard I try to stay on. How can I stop this from happening?

Emily

Dear Emily

Don't worry, this happens to lots of riders! If a pony bucks, most people think the best thing to do is to try to pull him up. Actually you're better off kicking him on and keeping his head up. Get your lower leg well forward, and sit back, like a Rodeo rider, so you don't get tipped off.

Pippa

Dear Pippa

I dream of being a champion rider one day, just like you. People tell me I'm good with horses, but what does it take to succeed?

Fiona

Dear Fiona

Stick at it. It took me until I was thirty-four to become the World Number One. You love horses and you're good with them, so that's a great start. Just remember, at your age it's important to have fun! Try not to dwell on your mistakes, just learn from them and build it from there.

Pippa

Racecourse Criss-Cross

Can you fit these well-known racecourse towns into the criss-cross puzzle below?

4 letters	7 letters	9 letters
YORK	NEWBURY	NEWMARKET
BATH	AINTREE	UTTOXETER

5 letters	8 letters
ASCOT	BRIGHTON
EPSOM	CHEPSTOW
	GOODWOOD

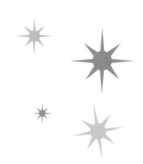

TILLY'S TOP TIP

Start by filling in the 9-letter word and the 7-letter word that both begin with the same letter

Points of a Pony

The parts of a pony or a horse are called 'points'. If you're having riding lessons, your instructor will use these names, so it's really useful to know the main points.

KEY

1. poll	11. flank	21. fetlock joint
2. ear	12. tail	22. cannon bone
3. eye	13. tendons	23. knee
4. mane	14. hock joint	24. shoulder
5. crest	15. stomach	25. chin groove
6. withers	16. elbow	26. nostril
7. back	17. heel	27. muzzle
8. loins	18. hoof	28. nose
9. croup	19. coronet band	29. cheekbone
10. dock	20. pastern	30. forelock

All About Horses Crossword

Have fun filling in this general knowledge crossword all about horses – both real and fictional.

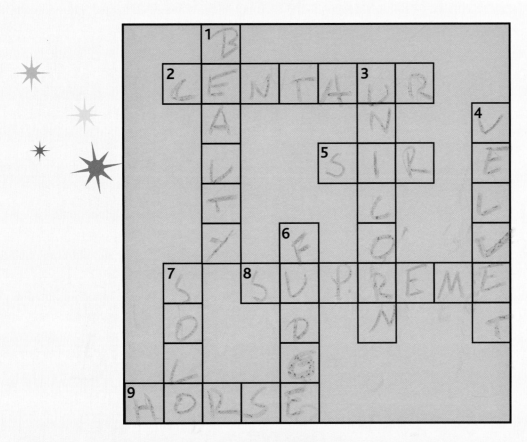

Across

2. A mythical creature that is part human, part horse.
5. Pippa's first horse was called __ __ __   BARNABY.
8. Pippa won the Badminton Horse Trials riding __ __ __ __ __ __ __   ROCK.
9. THE __ __ __ __ __   WHISPERER is Tilly's favourite film.

Down

1. BLACK __ __ __ __ __ __ is a famous story written in the horse's own voice.
3. A mythical horse-like creature with one horn.
4. NATIONAL __ __ __ __ __ __ is a well-known book and film about a girl who rides in the Grand National.
6. Cally's new pony at Cavendish Hall is called MR __ __ __ __ __ .
7. The name of Brook's horse.

Pippa's Pals

Emma and Keffy

Philippa and Sophie on Harold and Rocky

Isabelle and Lucy

Lucy

Callum on Topaz

Amber and Sadie

Emily with Candy

Annabel

Anna on Diva

Abbie
and
Archie

Izzy and Smartie

Phoebe on Larni

Cross-Country Maze

Can you ride Solo through the maze to the Finishing Post? Solo can jump over the stone walls, but he's spooked by the water jumps, so they are dead-ends and can't be crossed.

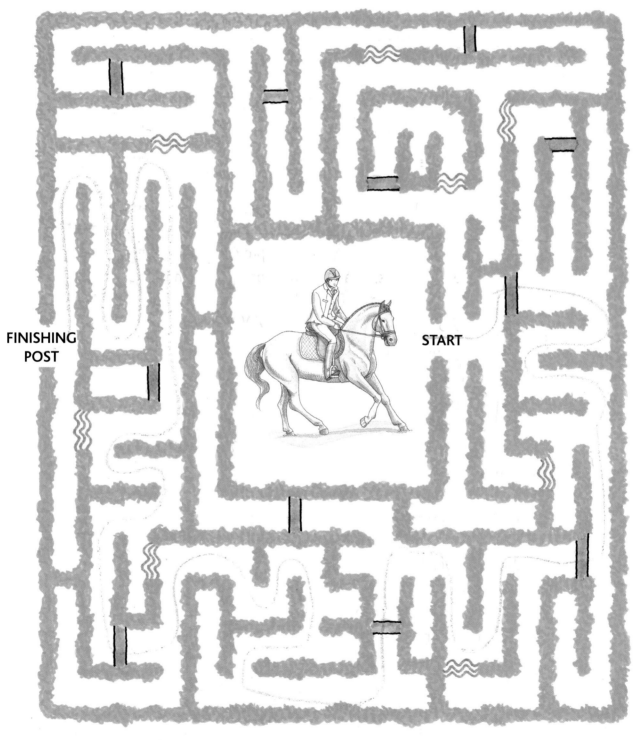

FINISHING POST

START

Water jumps 〜〜 **STOP!** **Stone walls** ▭ **GO!**

Pippa's Top Tips for Winter

PIPPA SAYS

It's cold and the days are shorter, but you can still enjoy your pony in the winter. Just follow my tips to stay safe and keep your pony warm and comfortable.

Riding

- Watch out for ice! If your pony has to walk over an icy surface, cover the ground with salt sand.
- Avoid riding on the roads when it's icy. Even if you can see the ice and avoid it, car drivers may not be able to.
- If you can't avoid being on the roads, wear reflective clothing.
- Don't let your pony get too hot and sweaty – at this time of year he could easily catch a chill.

Grooming

- If your pony does get sweaty, let him dry naturally, then remove all the dry sweat using a dandy brush.
- Avoid washing your pony in the cold weather, because you'll wash the vital protective oils out of his coat that help keep him warm.
- Use a plastic curry comb to scrape any mud off your pony. Check his legs for mud fever (sores where the hair on his legs fall out), caused by standing in muddy fields. Call the vet if you spot symptoms.
- Keep an eye on your pony's feet. He might get a bit foot-sore if the ground is frozen solid.

Stabling

- If your pony is in a stable at night always remember to have a good, dry bed.
- A healthy pony doesn't mind the cold weather, even if he's kept outside, but he will hate wet and windy weather. Make sure you provide shelter from the wind and the rain or a cosy turn-out rug.

Feeding

- There's very little grass in the winter, so you'll need to feed your pony with hay instead. When it's really cold, you may need to give your pony hard feed too.
- Don't forget your pony's water might ice up in the winter, so check and break and remove the ice every day if necessary.

Horses need special care all year round, so check out my tips for Spring on page 19, Summer on page 31 and Autumn on page 43.

At an event with my beautiful lorry!!

A great day was had by all at Olympia last Christmas

Signing books at
Badminton on the
World Horse
Welfare Stand

A Horse in Distress

When Tilly wins a backstage tour at the Christmas Olympia Horse Show, she loses sight of the tour group when she hears a horse in distress...

Tilly stared at a label that was attached to the door. It said 'Samson' in typed letters, and underneath that: 'Beware'.

"Hello there, Samson. I'm Tilly. What's the matter with you? I might be able to help. What's up?"

The horse stopped thrashing. He didn't look at Tilly, but she could tell that he was aware of her. She remembered how Magic Spirit had gradually responded to her attention. Becoming more and more confident around her, once he was sure she was a friend.

She took hold of her horsehair bracelet and felt Magic's tail hairs between her fingers. Was he okay? she wondered. She had been so excited by everything that was happening at Olympia, she hadn't had the chance to worry about him. Suddenly it all came flooding back.

"Please be okay when I get home," she whispered. "Please be better."

The horse in the stall became completely still. He pricked up his ears. It seemed he was listening to her. Maybe he felt sorry for Magic Spirit too.

Instinctively, Tilly undid the bolt that secured the door. She crept inside and reached her hand out. Slowly, the horse came to her. He leaned his nose towards her outstretched hand and began to explore it, nibbling and sniffing and getting used to her smell. His breath warmed her skin.

"That's it, Samson. Good boy. That's better. Take your time."

Samson gave a small snort and lifted his head. His face, which had been ferocious, was now relaxed. It was as if he was entranced. Tilly watched as the muscle tension in his body completely disappeared.

She stood beside him, and as she stroked his shoulders and back, she told him all about Magic Spirit – what a wonderful horse he was and how she hoped that he would make a full recovery from his colic. Samson listened patiently, rubbing his nose against Tilly's neck, and even letting her take some hair from his tail. I'll make a bracelet later, she thought.

Soon, they had lost all track of time and were responding to each other as though they were the oldest of friends.

"What do you think you're doing?"

Does Tilly get into terrible trouble? Find out in Samson the stallion.

Focus on Samson

Colour: Brown

Breed: Dutch

Appearance: Large, powerful stallion, with a well-groomed, shimmering coat of velvety brown

Personality: Spirited, bold and super-talented, but also has a wild side and a bad temper

Special info: When he jumps, he moves 'like rippling water, graceful and rhythmic'

Read **Samson** to find out if Tilly can work her magic on Samson at the Olympia Horse Show.

Top Point Ponies

Here's a card game for two players that's lots of fun to make and play. The aim of the game is to take all the cards off your opponent by always holding the card with the Top Point Pony.

You will need

Card
Scissors
Horse or pony pictures from magazines,
   or your own photos
Felt pens or crayons
Glue

 1 Cut out twelve cards, 10 x 6 cm.

 2 Cut out the pony pictures you've chosen, and glue one to each of the cards.

 3 Now you need to give each pony a list of points, like the sample Magic Spirit card below.

 4 If you don't know all the information for the list, don't worry – you can just make it up!

 5 You could add to your collection of cards whenever you find a nice pony picture you'd like to include.

MAGIC SPIRIT

- Height: **16 hh**
- Number of competitions won: **none**
- Age: **4 years**
- Top speed: **35 kmph**
- Star potential: ☆ ☆ ☆ ☆ ☆

ROSIE

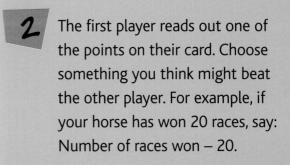

SAMSON
- Height: **17 hh**
- Number of competitions won: **4**
- Age: **11 years**
- Top speed: **30 kmph**
- Star potential: ☆ ☆ ☆ ☆

How to play

1 Deal the cards out equally between yourself and the other player. Keep your cards in front of you, face down on the table.

2 The first player reads out one of the points on their card. Choose something you think might beat the other player. For example, if your horse has won 20 races, say: Number of races won – 20.

3 If the other player has a horse that has won fewer than 20 races, they must hand over their card to you. If their horse has won more than 20 races, hand your card to them. The winner of the round should put both the cards at the bottom of their pile.

4 The game continues until one of the players has taken all the cards, and wins the game.

Duncan's Guide to Grooming

It's important to groom your pony to keep the skin healthy and the coat shiny – and most ponies really enjoy it too! Duncan makes it fun for the girls at Silver Shoe Farm by turning it into a guessing game.

Grooming Kit

There's a different piece of kit for each job.

Body brush

A soft brush for cleaning the grease and dust out of your pony's coat. It can be used all over the body.

Dandy brush

A stiff-bristled brush for loosening dried mud and sweat.

Hoof pick

Use this for cleaning out stones, dirt and mud from your pony's feet.

Mane and tail comb

Once you've loosened the dirt, use this to comb your pony's mane and tail, taking care not to pull tail hairs out.

Metal curry comb

Only to be used for scraping out the body brush – not to be used on your pony.

Sponge

For gently cleaning the eyes, nose and dock area (under the tail), and for when you give your pony a shampoo.

Mane pulling comb

Use this comb if your pony's mane is very thick and untidy. Wrap a few of the long hairs from underneath around the comb and pull them out.

Stable rubber

Use this cloth to remove any remaining scurf, to smooth your pony's coat and make it shine.

Plastic curry comb

For cleaning the body brush. It can also be used on your pony if she is covered in thick mud.

Hoof Oil and Brush

Paint on to your pony's hooves to protect them and make them shine.

Grooming Order

Always groom each pony in the same order each time, working from the top of the head to the hindquarters, and doing first one side and then the other.

1 Loosen the dirt on the pony's coat.

2 Comb the pony's mane and tail, also to loosen the dirt.

3 Brush the pony's coat to get rid of the dirt.

4 Then smooth the pony's coat to make it gleam.

5 Comb your pony's mane and tail again, using conditioning spray.

6 Check your pony's legs and clean her hooves.

7 Finally, paint hoof oil on to her clean, dry hooves.

Which Brush?

Duncan's Grooming Guessing Game

Which piece of grooming kit should you use for which job?

1 Rosie's mane is far too thick.

2 Magic Spirit has returned from a ride covered in thick mud.

3 The body brush needs cleaning.

4 Angela has asked to see Red Admiral's coat gleaming.

5 Rosie's hooves need to look their best for the Cosford races.

6 Bunny Hop has been riding along a path of loose stones.

7 Lulabelle has some dried mud and sweat on her coat. What would you use first?

8 You want to spoil Rosie with some grooming.

9 Magic Spirit's tail is untidy.

10 Red Admiral has mud around his eyes.

A

B

C

D

E

F

G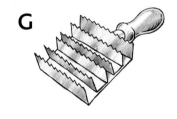

H

I

J

My Top Secret Diary
By Tiger Lily Redbrow

Tuesday 6th December 2011

It's nearly Christmas – hooray! I can't wait. Me and Becky are going Christmas shopping on our own on Saturday. I've been saving up my pocket money for ages to buy presents for Mum and Dad and Adam. I want to buy Magic Spirit a present too – it has to be something extra-special. If I've enough money left, I'll buy Rosie a cosy winter blanket just for being so lovely.

In the holidays, I'll be able to go to Silver Shoe Farm and see Rosie and Magic Spirit and all the other horses nearly every day. Brilliant! Mia will be there too. It's more fun when we do the mucking out and grooming together.

So much has happened this year. I've discovered that horses like me as much as I like them, and my dream of having riding lessons has finally come true. I don't think I've ever felt happier!

Next year, I'm going to try really, really hard to improve my riding. Then one day my dream of competing in a big event with Magic and winning might come true. I'd love to win medals – and maybe even enter the Olympics one day. Who knows?

How Much Do You Know About Ponies?

When you've been involved with horses as long as Pippa, you'll know lots and lots about them, and still learn new things every day. But you might already know more than you think. Try this multiple choice quiz and find out.

1. What's the best colour for a beginner's horse?

(a) Chestnut
(b) Grey
(c) It doesn't matter

2. Which of these is the fastest movement?

(a) Trot
(b) Canter
(c) Walk

3. How long could you expect a domestic horse to live?

(a) 25-30 years
(b) 5-10 years
(c) 45-50 years

4. Which is the smallest?

(a) Thoroughbred
(b) Connemara
(c) Shetland

5. Which of these is *not* a horse's coat colour?

(a) Bay
(b) Chestnut
(c) Yellow

6. When you go looking for your first ever pony, who's the best person to take with you?

(a) An experienced horse person
(b) Your best friend
(c) Your mum or dad

7. Which of these animals is part of the horse family?

(a) Giraffe
(b) Zebra
(c) Deer

8. How long does it take before a foal can stand up?

(a) A few days
(b) A couple of weeks
(c) Within an hour

9. What's another name for the saddle cloth that goes under the saddle?

(a) Numnah
(b) Skirt
(c) Saddle flap

10. A hand is a unit of measurement that is used to measure a pony's height. How many inches are there in a hand?

(a) 4 inches
(b) 6 inches
(c) 8 inches

Check the answers on page 75, and add up your grand total.

If you scored between 1 and 4

A good try, but there's still lots for you to learn about horses and ponies. If you read Tilly's Pony Tails, you'll find them full of pony info and discover all sorts of new things about the world of ponies while you enjoy reading the books.

If you scored between 5 and 7

Well done, you're already pretty knowledgeable about horses and ponies. You've probably read and enjoyed all the Tilly's Pony Tails books! Why not try to spend more time grooming and riding horses at the stables too, and you'll pick up lots of tips along the way.

If you scored between 8 and 10

Top class, you deserve a rosette! Horses and ponies are obviously a big part of your life and you already know plenty about them. Keep up the good work when you're at the stables and have fun reading all the new books in the Tilly's Pony Tails series.

For more tips, quizzes, fun facts and sneak previews of the new books, join the Tilly's Pony Tails Club at

www.tillyponystails.co.uk

Planet Pony – Tilly's Favourite Facts

When Tilly's not with the horses at Silver Shoe Farm, she's reading about horses and visiting lots of pony websites too! Here are Tilly's top ten favourite facts:

1 Horses can sleep standing up. They lock their back legs in position so that they don't fall over.

2 The oldest recorded horse in the UK was Old Billy who lived until he was 62, after a life pulling barges on the canal. Normally, horses live about 25-30 years.

3 The fastest horses can gallop up to 50 miles per hour.

4 Horses have an official birthday on 1 January.

5 The largest horse ever recorded was Sampson, a Shire horse, who was 22½ hands high and weighed around 1,520kg. His owners later changed his name to Mammoth!

6 Ponies need to drink 30 litres of water every day – that's about 3½ buckets full.

7 A red ribbon in a horse's tail warns people not to get too close because it kicks. A green ribbon warns people it's a young horse.

8 Within an hour, a newborn foal can stand up and within twenty-four hours, it can keep up with the rest of the horses.

9 Horses will often stand tail to tail and shelter each other from annoying flies by swishing their tails for each other!

10 Horses can see a long way behind them because their eyes are on the sides of their head.

Puzzle Answers

Page 14
Tilly's Pony Tails Wordsearch

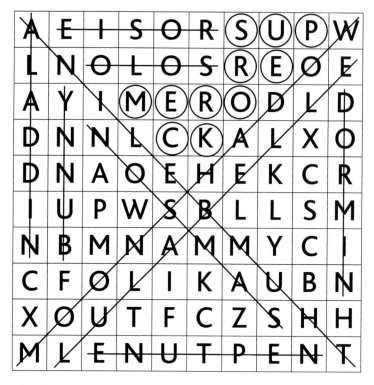

The hidden name is SUPREME ROCK

Page 28
Tack Terms Wordsearch

Page 30
Breeds Criss-Cross

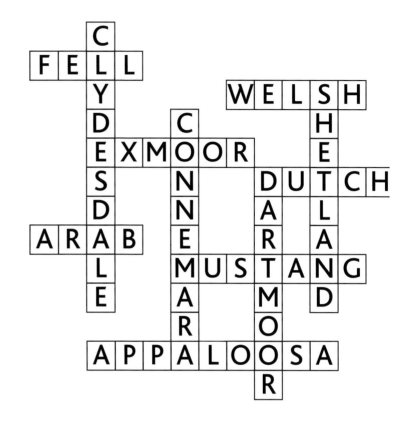

Page 51
Racecourse Criss-Cross

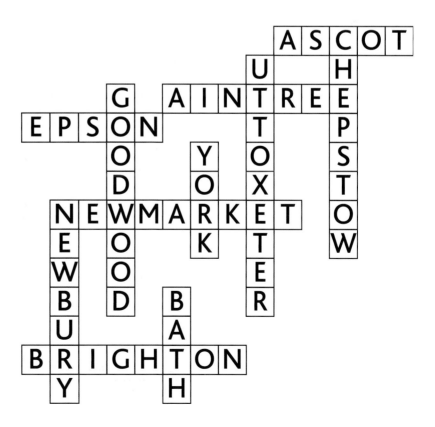

Page 53
All About Horses Crossword

Page 56
Cross-country Maze

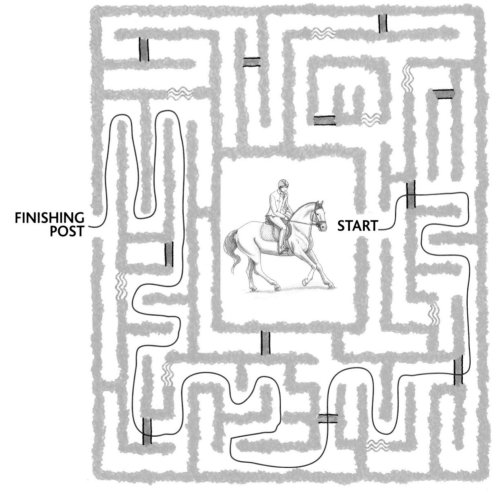

Page 66

Duncan's Grooming Guessing Game

1 = D	6 = H
2 = C	7 = A
3 = G	8 = F
4 = E	9 = J
5 = I	10 = B

Page 68

How Much Do You Know About Ponies?

1. (c)	6. (a)
2. (b)	7. (b)
3. (a)	8. (c)
4. (c)	9. (a)
5. (c)	10. (b)

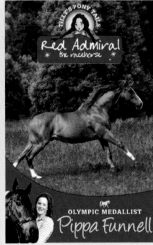

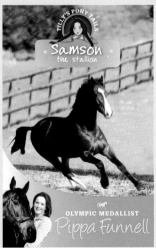

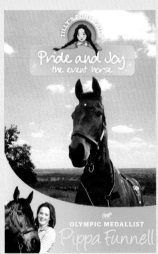

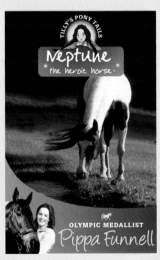

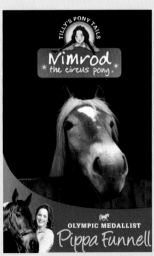

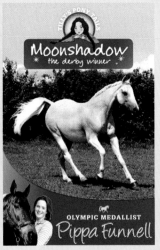

from September
2010

from November
2010

from January
2011

from March
2011

**YOU CAN JOIN THE
TILLY'S PONY TAILS CLUB AT**

Visit the website for more about Pippa, Tilly and Silver Shoe Farm – plus Pippa's newsletter, competitions and everything you ever wanted to know about horses.

Thanks to everyone who
sent in their photographs to the website.
Keep sending them, and you might
appear in next year's Annual!